This book is for:

Zak

I saw you, I see you and I will always see you

close or far you
will always be my
friend. I love you,
Lucas.

**To Hazel and Heike,
Your infinite empathy will
always inspire me.**

First edition published in United Kingdom in 2021 by The Lemon Planet.

Translated to English by Hazel Kenny

Copyright © Lucia Salom Velásquez, 2022

ISBN: 978-1-8381006-4-3

I see you

Luci Salom

I am part of the place where you belong.

Your ideas and everything you undertake, I find unique and meaningful, and also admirable.

Even when you reinvent or change your own goals and resolutions, you keep persevering.

That is why I have been, continue to be, and always will be witness to your small and big achievements.

That's because I see you, I hear you and I value you.

It has always mattered to me, and always will, how you have felt in the past or how you will feel in the future.

Maybe I have not always found or will not always find the right words.

I may not have always managed to fully understand you or may not always be able to in the future.

However, I have no doubt that I will always be here for you.

Always.

So...

If you feel like you are a complete mess

When you are scared

When you feel the greatest pride

If you feel weighed down by
disappointment

When you are sad

When you feel happy

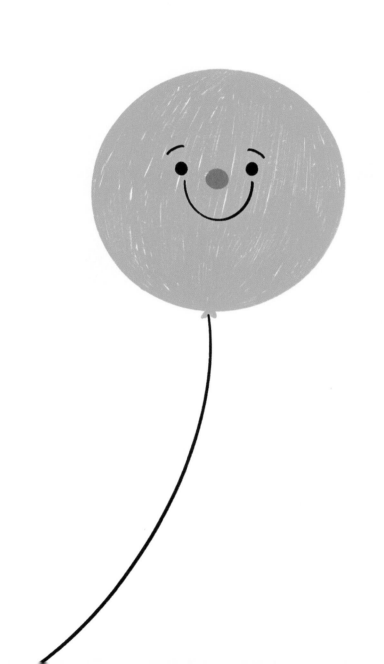

If you feel at peace

When you're overcome by anger

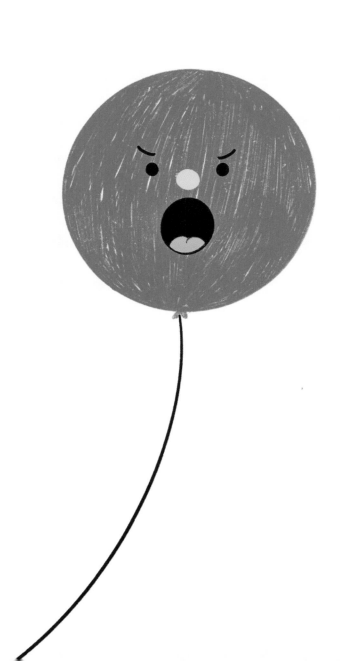

When you feel a sense of achievement

When you think you couldn't be more frustrated

If you form strong connections

If you feel completely isolated

When insecurity takes over

When fear takes hold of you

If you feel it was all worth it

**When you think that your efforts
were in vain**

When you feel fulfilment

When you feel like you have a pit in
your stomach

When you're about to explode

If at any time you are suffering

When you feel inspired

If you can't find your way

If you feel guilty

When you feel the problems won't let you sleep

When you feel enormous

When you feel insignificant

If you are about to take on a new challenge

When you are at the point of giving up

When you feel you are different

If you feel invisible

When enthusiasm sweeps in

When you feel nothing but
exhaustion

When you're bored to death

When you want to have fun

When you need quiet

When you feel the need to talk

Words

Words

Words

If you don't feel at all well

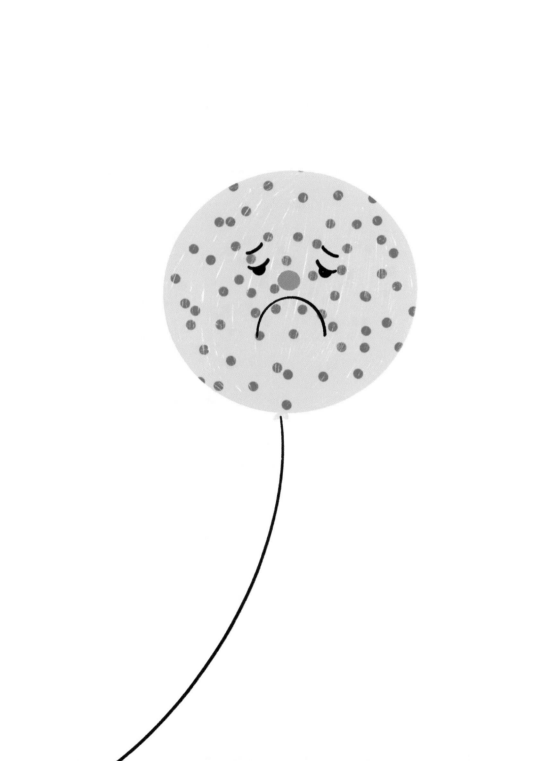

When you feel fantastic

When you're overcome by nostalgia

Even when you can't put your finger
on how you're feeling

Come and find me, and never doubt that you can share with me. I am here for you and always will be.

Surely you will see that my expression resembles yours, because I understand how you feel and because your emotions are contagious to me.

I see you, I hear you, I value and I love you.

Yesterday, today and always.